# RAVEN-
## WHO-SETS-THINGS-RIGHT

A revised edition, with all new art,
of NINE TALES OF RAVEN

# RAVEN-
## WHO-SETS-THINGS-RIGHT

Indian Tales of the Northwest Coast

Retold by FRAN MARTIN

Pictures by Dorothy McEntee

HARPER & ROW, Publishers

New York — Evanston — San Francisco — London

# Contents

The People Who Told the Tales    1

1   In the Beginning        11

2   Raven Lets Out the Daylight        17

3   The Unlucky Fisherman        27

4   The Nose of the Konakadet        37

5   Cannibal        45

6   The Mountain Goats        53

7   Strong-Man        61

8   The False Shaman        69

9   Eagle Boy        75

10  The Everlasting House        83

Acknowledgments        89

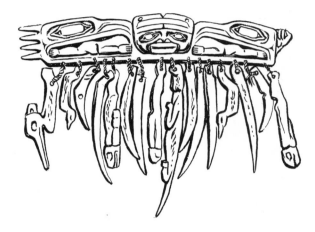

*Shaman's necklace hung with magic charms. Similar charms face each chapter opening.*

# The People Who Told the Tales

The Indians who told these stories of Raven lived far up in the northwest corner of North America, along the coast of the Pacific Ocean. Tlingit, Haida, Tsimshian, and Kwakiutl Indians live there still, but the tales in this book are adapted from versions told by native storytellers near the beginning of this century, before the tribes had much contact with non-Indian culture.

The Northwest Coast Indians developed unique ways of living within their environment. Although their only tools were made of sharpened shell and stone, they learned to use fire, carefully controlled, to fell tremendous cedar trees, which they used to build huge, tightly constructed houses big enough for six to ten families. Fifty or sixty people might live in such a house, full as it was of the scent of salmon and the smoke of cedar logs smoldering in the shallow pit in the middle.

There was too much rain for ordinary farming, but the people had no need to grow their food. They lived well on succulent roots, shoots, and berries, and on the bounty of the sea—salmon and sea lions, herring and whales and seals. That bounty was so rich, and they gathered and stored it with such skill, that they were able to build up a surplus every summer and live in comfort all the rest of the year.

The months of winter leisure gave them time to ponder about the world—filled, as they saw it, with animals and men, and supernatural creatures that could take the shape of either. There were hundreds of tales about their world and how it began, and the stories were polished over the years by telling and retelling around the house fire, until every child came to know every word. The tales were both history and science to them.

It was on winter nights, when the evening meal was done, that the great carved houses would come alive. The fire, fed by grease from the evening's cooking, would crackle and flare, and a trail of smoke rising up to the smoke hole would make the carved animals on the house posts seem to writhe and wink their abalone eyes. Then all the cousins would gather close, and the best of the tellers of tales— man or woman, but often one of the Old Ones—would begin.

If this was a Tlingit household, the storyteller might start off with a tale about Raven the Creator. The Tlingits believed it was Raven who had created the Sun, Moon, Stars, and Earth, and there were said to be so many Raven tales that life was not long enough to tell them all. The Haida, Tsimshian, and Kwakiutl Indians had different Creation stories, sometimes more than one. As with any tales passed on by word of mouth, various tellers would drop an ending here or make a new combination there; and the stories in this book have been altered and combined in the same way.

2

There were many other stories of Raven as the Transformer, a creature half-bird, half-man, who went about completing the half-made world—Raven-Who-Sets-Things-Right. In such tales, Raven often turns into a scamp who enjoys outwitting the same trusting creatures he has been trying to help. And since all the world enjoys seeing such a character get a dose of his own medicine, the underdog in the story often manages to turn the tables.

While many of the Northwest Coast stories are about Raven-Who-Sets-Things-Right, there are hundreds of funny anecdotes in which Raven has still another role, as Raven the Trickster. Sometimes he plays both parts in the same story. Raven the Trickster is vain and pompous and endlessly hungry, and often his victims make him look like a fool.

Other myths explained the natural world. The Indians believed that animals lived like men; for instance, sea monsters lurked in the ocean, with a chief called the Konakadet, and there was a village of Killer Whales, and a King Crab as big as a house. The Salmon lived farther out, in orderly villages on the bottom of the sea, and went about their business in the form of men.

Mountain Goats and Grizzly Bears were thought to live in houses hidden deep in the dense forest, as well as even stranger supernatural creatures like Cannibal and Woman-Rooted-to-the-Floor. Not only could the animals take on the form of men, but they also had magic power. Whenever one of them wished to be alone, he could slip into his animal cloak and mask and pad off into the forest.

Each family had its own special story about a long-ago

*Dance masks representing animals and spirits were worn when the great myths were told. They were carved from wood, painted, and often decorated with shells, bark fringes, feathers, or fur.*

ancestor—how he met with a supernatural creature, be it Beaver, Bear, or Killer Whale, who became his guardian spirit and gave him a magic treasure to be passed down through the generations. Such stories belonged to one family or clan that thought itself descended from the hero of the story. That family could claim the supernatural creature

as its guardian spirit, and use a symbolic carving of that
animal as its crest. If the family was rich and important
enough to have a totem pole, the crest would be carved
there, interlocked with other animal crests the family
claimed.

In stories like "The Mountain Goats," "Eagle Boy,"

and "Strong-Man," the animal guardian spirit always ends by bestowing on the hero a song, a dance, a certain ritual, to be handed down in the family along with the story itself and the crest. Tangible objects might be given too, like a fine carved house stocked with spoons and wooden dishes, berries boxed in oil, and dried salmon. But it was the spiritual gifts that counted most, and young people of the house, boys and girls alike, were encouraged to fast, bathe in icy water, and endure night-long vigils in the hope of being approached by the family's guardian spirit again.

During the long winter, every man and woman had time to become an artist or a craftsman, to the limit of his talents. The women did the weaving and basketry; they could weave baskets tight enough to hold water. Among the men, the great arts were cabinet work and carving. They could make a box or chest out of a single long plank, so tight it could be used for cooking by pouring in water and adding red-hot stones. But cabinet work was only the beginning. They wanted every possible surface carved with representations of the figures of the myths, arranged in powerful, flowing patterns. The design conformed to the shape of the object, whether they were carving a ten-foot screen or the handle of a sheephorn ladle. To represent one of the sacred animals, they created special symbols which could be instantly understood. Beaver would always be shown with two big front teeth, a stick, and a cross-hatched tail. Bear had big paws and a lolling tongue. Raven had a long, straight beak, while Eagle's beak was curved. A dorsal fin would stand for Killer Whale. But if the artist set out to show the whole animal, it was traditional to show all four legs, as well as two eyes, two ears, and both sides of its head. This was no problem on a house post. But to fit the shape of a box or screen, the artist might use a kind of X-ray view, showing the animal split down back or front and spread out flat, sometimes with stylized lungs or intestines drawn in, and designs at the joints that looked like eyes.

Working within these strict rules, these gifted peoples created a splendid and fantastic art unequaled in North America. When the nineteenth-century fur traders brought in steel tools, Northwest Coast art surged to new heights. The traditional house post developed into a so-called totem pole, up to eighty feet tall. This pole, with its column of animal designs, became the trademark of the Northwest Coast.

A totem pole might be raised for a "potlatch" ceremony given to honor a dead chief and to call to public witness the credentials of his successor. This long and elaborate ceremony would be staged in the winter, since winter was set aside for sacred things. It was a lavish four-day feast with songs and dances, where marvelous masks and costumes were displayed, gifts were given to every guest, and the myth about the founder of the family's encounter with the supernatural creature that became his guardian spirit was told again.

Picture the scene when the great day of a potlatch comes at last. The guests from another village, arriving in a flotilla of carved dugout canoes, are met by dancers on the beach. They dance in their turn, and there is an exchange of speeches. Then, stooping to enter through the oval door-way, they leave the sun and wind of the beach behind and find themselves in a great smoky cavern packed with people. High above, a dazzling square of light marks the smoke hole. Half led, half pushed, the stranger stumbles in and is guided to his proper seat.

Faces begin to come clear through the darkness. The Chief of the host village sits in the place of honor, behind the fire and facing the door, with the Speaker, the Song Leader, and other important men. Behind them is the sacred room, its panels carved and painted with the household crest. Up under the roof are platforms reached by ladders; children watch from there.

All are seated, and silence falls. The Chief's wife feeds the fire with bear fat. The flames leap up and the firelight flickers on house posts carved with huge faces and staring eyes.

A drum begins to boom as a swaddled fist beats on the hanging box, and the people join in with a rhythmic clap-ping. Close to the fire, the Chiefs and the Old Ones beat time with their dancing staffs. The Song Leader starts up the chanting, and the men and boys join in as the pounding stops. They sing for the living, and they sing for the dead; they sing for the Chief who is dead and for his young successor.

The door flap opens with a sudden streak of daylight, and four monstrous masked figures come whirling in, to do the ancient dances. There is a pause at the end, and the Song Leader takes the chorus through the intricate songs of the guardian spirit of the house. Then the Speaker rises.

He waits for words to come, while the people tremble and draw close. A gust of wind seizes the house and shakes it, and the surf booms loud on the rocks. And so it starts:

"In the beginning, there was nothing but soft darkness . . ."

The two-day telling has begun.

*Haida design from a shirt shows Wolf split down the middle and spread out flat to display both sides of the head and all four paws. The X-ray vision of the lungs and intestines is typical of Northwest Coast art.*

# 1 In the Beginning

In the beginning there was nothing but soft darkness, and
Raven beat and beat with his wings until the darkness
packed itself down into solid earth. Then there was only
the icy black ocean and a narrow strip of shoreline. But
people came soon to live along the coast. And Raven felt
sorry for them, poor, sickly things, who never had any
sunshine. They lived by chewing on nuts and leaves,
and crushed the roots of the alder trees for something
to drink.

"I must help them," thought Raven; and he flew down
to earth, calling, "*Ga, ga, ga!*" and gathered the people
together. Like ghosts, they were, shadowy and pale in the
misty darkness.

"Raven has come!" they told each other. "It is Raven-
Who-Sets-Things-Right."

The poor things were encouraged, and they gathered
round to see what he would do.

Raven plucked a branch from an alder, and scattered
the leaves on the surface of a pool. At once the leaves were
sucked under, and the water started to bubble. After the
pool had boiled for a moment, the surface cleared and fish

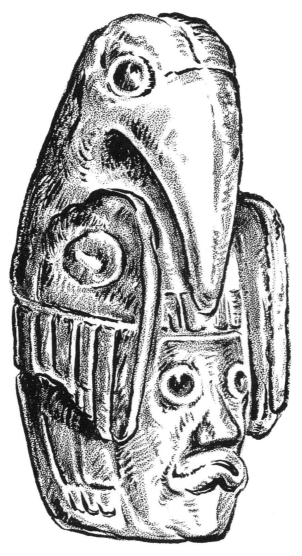

*Tlingit stone carving of Raven in both man and bird forms.*

began to jump there. So that was how Raven gave the people fish.

But now that they had fish to eat, they were thirstier than ever. They called on Raven, and down he came, and the people said, "Here is Raven-Who-Sets-Things-Right."

Raven knew that there was only one spring of fresh water in all the world. A man named Ganook had built his house around it, and refused to give any away.

"Maybe," thought Raven, "I can drink enough to carry some back to the people."

So he went to the house and asked to come in, and Ganook was very glad to have his company. Raven sat down and made polite conversation, and pretty soon he asked for a drink of water.

"Very well," said Ganook grudgingly, and showed him the spring, a crystal pool welling up in a basin of rock.

"Don't drink it all!" Ganook warned him. "You know that's the only fresh water in all the world."

Raven knew it well; that was what he had come for. But he said, "Just a sip!" and drank until he staggered.

"Hold on there, Raven!" cried Ganook. "Are you trying to drink the well dry?"

That was just what Raven was trying to do, but he passed it off lightly. He made himself comfortable close to the fire and said, "Ganook, let me tell you a story."

Then Raven started out on a long dull story about four dull brothers who went on a long dull journey. As he went along he made up dull things to add to it, and Ganook's eyelids drooped, and Raven spoke softly, and more and more slowly, and Ganook's chin dropped on his chest.

13

"So then," said Raven gently, with his eyes on Ganook, "on and on through the long gray valley through the soft gray fog went the four tall gray brothers. And now, snore!" And Ganook began to snore.

Quick as a thought, Raven darted to the spring and stuck his beak into the water. But no sooner had he lifted his head to swallow than Ganook started up with a terrible snort, and said, "Go on, go on, I'm listening! I'm not asleep." Then he shook his head and blinked his eyes and said, "Where are you, Raven? What are you doing?"

"Just walking around for exercise," Raven assured him, and back he went, and in a low, unchanging voice he went on with the long dull story of the four brothers. No sooner had he started than Ganook began to nod, and his chin dropped down, and he jerked it back and opened his eyes and scowled at Raven, and nodded his head and said, "Go on! What next?" and his head dropped down upon his chest.

"So on and on," said Raven slowly, "over the hills, went the four tall gray brothers. The air was thick and gray around them. Fog was stealing softly over the mountains. Fog before them, fog behind them, soft, cloudy fog. And now, snore!" And Ganook began to snore.

Quietly Raven slipped to the spring, and, *glub, glub, glub,* he drank up the water until the pool was dry. But as he lifted his head for a last long gulp, Ganook leaped up and saw what he was doing.

"So, Raven!" shouted Ganook. "You think you can lull me to sleep and steal my water!"

He picked up his club and started to chase Raven round and round the fire. Raven would run a few steps and flap his big wings and rise a few inches off the floor. Then with a last tremendous flap he went sailing toward the open smoke hole. But he had swallowed so much water that he stuck fast in the opening, and there he struggled, while Ganook shouted, "You squint-eyed Raven, I've got you now, Raven! You miserable thief!" And Ganook threw green alder logs on the fire and made a great smoke which came billowing up and almost choked Raven to death.

Raven hung there, strangling and struggling, until at last he pulled free with a mighty wrench and went wobbling heavily off across the sky. He was so heavy he flew in a crooked line, and as he flew he spurted little streams of water from his bill. These became rivers, first the Nass and the Sitka, then the Taku and the Iskut and the Stikine. Since Raven flew in a crooked line, all the rivers are crooked as snakes. Here and there he scattered single drops, and these became narrow creeks and salmon pools.

And so Raven brought fresh water to the people—but he bore the mark of that smoke hole ever after. He had gone to Ganook as a great, white, snowy creature, but from that day on, Raven was black, as black as the endless sky of the endless night.

## 2 Raven Lets Out the Daylight

Now Raven had made the rivers and filled them with fish, but still the people suffered. They had to do all their fishing in the dark, and they fished all the time, for there was nothing else to eat. Raven felt sorry for them, poking about in the everlasting darkness. So down he came, saying, "I am Raven-Who-Sets-Things-Right."

Raven knew that the Sun and the Moon and the Stars were hidden in the house of the Old-One-at-the-Source-of-the-River. He was determined to steal this light and give it to the people.

So Raven turned himself into a little baby and had himself born of the only daughter of the Old-One-at-the-Source-of-the-River. But he was no ordinary baby. On the second day he stood up in his basket; he crawled on the third day and walked on the fourth, and although he never said a word but *"Ga!"* the Old-One was even more doting and proud than grandfathers are today.

"Look at those eyes!" he said. "Sharp as a raven's!" But he never suspected that Raven himself had become a member of the family.

One thing bothered the Old-One and his daughter: the

baby refused to eat. They tried him on deer fat, mutton fat, and tallow, for inside that house was all the wealth of future generations. Coming from above as Raven did, he had no need to eat. But although the baby was growing so fast, his mother was sure he was going to die unless he started to eat. So she tried a trick. She knew that anyone who ate the fish called bullhead would be hungry ever after. The baby liked to sit with them and chew a piece of fat, so she folded a shred of bullhead in the fat, and Raven swallowed it down.

All at once the baby started to cry as human babies do, stuffing his fingers into his mouth and making sucking noises.

"Can it be true?" his mother cried. "I believe my baby is hungry!"

She gave him food, and the baby ate, and a few minutes later he was hungry again. This went on all day and all week, and soon the Old-One began to fret for fear he would use up all his provisions.

Then came a new trouble. High in the rafters, the sharp eyes of Raven discovered what he had come for. Three great bags swung there in the shadows, and he figured they were just about big enough to hold the Sun, the Moon, and the Stars.

"*Ga!*" said the baby, starting to cry, and he stretched his fat little arms toward the three great bags. His mother dandled him and rocked him and clucked in his ear, but nothing would make him stop.

"Father," said the Old-One's daughter at last, "why can't the baby play with the smallest bag?"

"No!" said the Old-One, but the baby kept on crying, and at last he could stand it no longer and gave him the bag.

The baby was quiet, rolling the bag about on the floor behind his mother. Then all at once he pulled the drawstring, and *whoosh!* the Stars swept up through the smoke hole and scattered to their places in the sky.

For some time after that the grandfather was angry, and the poor mother kept Raven as quiet as she could with enormous quantities of food. The shred of bullhead had done its work; Raven was a ravenous eater from that day forward.

Between feedings he did nothing but cry and stretch out his arms toward the remaining two bags that swung against the rafters. He cried until his eyes turned around in his head, and his mother was frantic with worry.

"You're not going to have them!" the Old-One thundered, but at last he took the second bag down from the hook and gave it to his grandson.

Raven was quiet, rolling the bag about on the earthen floor behind them. Then secretly he loosened the string, and *whisk!* the silvery disk of the Moon went spinning through the smoke hole.

The Old-One was sad, because now he had lost all but the last of his sacred treasures. And still the baby cried and cried as he stretched out his arms for the Sun bag. His mother was distracted, and the Old-One was afraid the baby was going to die.

"Take it, then!" he shouted, and threw him the bag— but first he tightened the cord.

Raven worked and worked on the knot, but there was

19

*Part of Haida totem pole shows Raven (top) bringing the sun and moon to the people.*

nothing he could do. So, "*Ga, ga, ga!*" he changed back to a Raven, seized the bag, and escaped through the smoke hole.

He flew and he flew until he came to the crooked river where all the people were fishing. And this time when Raven looked at the piles of fish gleaming like silver in the darkness, he was ravenously hungry.

"Give me some of your fish," he said to the people. "I'm feeling very hungry."

As soon as Raven wanted something for himself, the ungrateful people refused him.

"Catch your own fish," they told him rudely. "We have scarcely enough for ourselves."

"Come, now, just a little, and I'll let out the daylight!"

"Let out the daylight? You? You're Raven; you haven't any daylight. Get away!"

Raven went on down the river a bit, and begged fish of the next little group, for by now he was starving. But the answer was the same, on and on down the river, until he came to the last village, near the coast.

"*Ga, ga, ga!*" croaked Raven weakly. "Give me some fish, and I will let out the daylight!"

"Come, now, Raven; you can't let out the daylight! But all the same we'll help you if you're hungry." And they threw him a small pile of fish, which he devoured in a twinkling.

Then Raven said, "Cover your eyes with your fingers, now, for I'm letting out the daylight!"

They covered their eyes, and Raven tore at the Sun bag with his beak. First he made a small tear in the bag, and the

21

rays of the Sun shot out like jagged lightning. Then he caught the great round disk in his beak, and ripped it out of the bag!

A wave of light rushed over the world, and in all the canoes, up and down the river, the fishermen jumped to their feet. Canoes capsized on every side as they tried to shield their eyes. Some of the people dived overboard, and some of them leaped for the shore. Those that took to the water became seals and otters and sea lions, and those that took to the forest became forest creatures. And only those that gave Raven the fish continued to be men.

But instead of the weak, sickly creatures that had lived before in the world of darkness, these men were strong and vigorous and daring. They launched their canoes on the open ocean, and pitted their strength against the strength of sharks and whales. The drooping trees stretched up tall in the forest, and pale leaves, curled like the fronds of ferns, opened to drink the sunlight. Flowers sprang up in the grass like stars, and glittering insects hummed and drummed all day in the golden sunshine.

Then back flew Raven to the Source of the River to see what the Old-One thought about it now. He perched on a tree near the house of the Old-One and called to the Old-One's daughter.

"Come out, come out, my mother," said Raven, "and see what I've done to the world."

She came out, frightened.

"I've seen what you've done, and I think it is right, but my father is still in a rage. He sits in the house in his conjuror's hat and tries to conjure you back; and now he's done it. So fly away, Raven, before it's too late, or the Old-One will have his revenge upon us all."

"I won't fly away until he comes outdoors to see what the world is like."

His mother implored him to fly away home, but boldly he entered the house of the Old-One, with his mother following after. At first it was dark. He could make out nothing but the feeble flicker of the embers. But there on the bench, with his chin on his fist, glowering, sat the Old-One.

"Who is it that comes?" he growled without turning, and Raven answered, "Your grandson."

The Old-One sprang to his feet with a roar of anger.

"Grandson, you say! You're no grandson of mine, you Raven! You stole the Sun!"

"Come to the door, Old-One, and I'll show you what the Sun has done for the world!"

"Done for it, has it?" the Old-One shouted. "I'll show you what I can do!"

The Old-One gave his conjuror's hat a twist, and water gushed out of the top like a whirlpool and splashed in a circle on the floor and made a pool.

"Father, father!" cried Raven's mother. "Stop the water quickly, I beg you!"

But he gave his hat another twist, and the water gushed faster than ever. It filled the center of the huge house, and Raven and his mother climbed to the level of the rooms along the back. And as the house was filling the world was flooded, to the level of the foothills. The people and the forest creatures fled to the hills to escape the rising waters.

Then Raven's mother cried, "Father, I beg you! Stop it! Stop the flood!"

But the Old-One twisted his hat again, and the water gushed out in a torrent. Raven and his mother climbed up to a narrow shelf close under the roof. At the same time the whole earth was flooded, and the people and animals were crowded together on the tops of the highest mountains.

"Father!" cried Raven's mother again. "Let the waters go down!"

But the Old-One sat there and twisted his hat, and the waters filled the house to the very rafters. Then Raven changed his mother to a silver fish, and they both escaped through the smoke hole.

Raven flew out over a desolate waste, lashed by the slanting rain. All of the lush and sunshiny world had been washed away by the flood. The whole round circle was a tossing ocean, under a lowering sky. On flew Raven, heading for the mountains, and he saw that the top of the highest mountain was now an island in the waste. The dark figures of wolves and bears were slinking among the rocks; and as Raven flew over he heard a faint crying, a lonely sound almost lost in the roar of the tempest.

He circled back and found four small children, cowering for fear of the hungry beasts that were trapped on the mountain with them. Only these four little children were left, of all the flourishing tribes that had peopled the earth.

So Raven scooped them up with his claws, and flew up and up, to thrust his strong beak into the solid floor of the sky. He hung there until the rain stopped, and sheltered the four little children under his wings.

When a watery sun drank up the clouds, he called on his friend the Frog to come and dropped the children down on her broad green back. There they floated for twenty days more, until the water ran off the mountains in torrents and the children could wade ashore.

So it was that Raven saved the children from the flood, and these four children lived to be the parents of future generations.

# 3 The Unlucky Fisherman

In time, there were men in the world again, and animals as well. In those days the animals looked like men, but they had supernatural power. And the animals lived in towns like men—the Mountain Goats here, the Grizzly Bears there, the Salmon in great carved houses under the sea. So, if a creature wanted to be alone, he could slip into his animal skin and mask and take to the forest or the sea.

For the first hundred years or so after the flood, Raven had an easy life with his animal friends. But he began to hear disturbing news of the people. Half of them were sick and the other half stupid; they seemed to have little talent for running the world. Worst of all were the people of Crooked Beach.

"I am Raven," he said, "Raven-Who-Sets-Things-Right."

He knew he could help the people best if he lived with them as a shaman, a medicine man. He would cure the sick and foretell trouble. So he left his pleasant life with the animals and set off for Crooked Beach. He sought out a quiet pool behind the dunes, pushed back his Raven mask, slipped out of his feather cloak, and bent eagerly over the water to see his reflection.

At first poor Raven was bitterly disappointed. Instead of the strong young chief he had expected, the piercing black eyes of an old man stared back through the wavering water. The long beak he had worn as a Raven had become a shaman's jointed hat. Altogether, the sight of his human aspect gave Raven a jolt.

Then he thought to himself, "I'm as old as the world. Why should I expect to look like a stripling?" So he carved himself a shaman's staff and conjured up a house.

Since Raven and his hat had the look of a shaman, the people soon started coming for advice. He showed them where to set the fish traps and how to greet the First Salmon, and he taught the hunters to fast and purify themselves before setting out after bear or mountain sheep. And at daybreak every day he went, "Ga, ga, ga!" to drive away the ghosts and monsters that prowled in the night. Things went better at Crooked Beach, and most of the people prospered.

But there was one poor fisherman who never had any luck. His lines broke, his canoe sprang leaks, and when all the men went to the halibut grounds, he caught the smallest fish. With a scolding wife and three small nephews to support, the poor man was hard pressed. So at last he did what he should have done sooner: he went to Raven.

"Leave the village," Raven advised him. "Try a new place, and you may come back in the fall with supplies for the winter."

"My wife is afraid to go anywhere," the unlucky man objected. "She saw in a dream that the Otter People were to kidnap our nephews."

"Keep them off the water and you're safe," said Raven. "And keep them in after dark. Otter People are the spirits of drowned fishermen, and they roam the beaches at night. But if they're out of their holes when I call at daybreak, they die."

The unlucky fisherman did as he was told. He loaded his family into the leaky canoe with all their poor possessions. So they set out in the bright spring weather, but no sooner had they gone a good distance from home than the wind freshened and black clouds boiled, and great green combers came every which way, bursting with plumes of spray. The man and his wife struggled hard, and even the little boys, all together, tried to man one long oar. But a last towering wave capsized the canoe and hurled them all into the water.

The unlucky fisherman saved his wife, but the three little boys were lost. Then the poor man was hard to console, and his wife kept carping and throwing the blame on Raven. They spent the first night shaking on the sand as they listened to the ghostly whistling of the Otter People. But the sun dawned fair and warm next day, and by the second night they had thrown together a simple shelter.

The man made fishing lines of kelp, and halibut hooks of spruce wood dried in the fire. But now he had no canoe, and once again they lived on whatever the woman could find at low tide. She complained bitterly, but he was used to that and never even heard her scolding.

One day in the woods he picked up a flat piece of rock.

"Just right for an ax blade," he said to himself, and he

rubbed the edge very sharp with another rock. Then he bound the blade to a strong handle and looked around for a tree.

"Here's my canoe," he decided at last, and he started to chop away at a good-sized cedar. The first day he chipped a deep gash, then it was a wedge, and soon the tree came down. Still he said nothing about it at home, for he knew the woman would say he was wasting his time. He hacked it into the shape of a boat, and kept a fire burning on top until he was able to scoop the log out and make it hollow. Then he bound his blade to a shorter handle and chipped away happily, testing the sides between his hands to get an even thickness.

So the time passed pleasantly enough, except that he missed his three nephews and had so little to eat. One day he caught a fish from the rocks, and his wife hung most of it up to dry in the brush house. In the night they heard two loud thumps from that direction.

"Wife!" the man whispered. "Something is after our fish."

The wife remembered the Otter People, and kept him from going out. But at daybreak he ran outdoors and found two devilfish stranded.

"Wife!" he shouted. "We are in luck! Devilfish for bait!"

But the woman was staring. "Look!" she said. "They're lying above the high-tide mark! Somebody put them there!"

"Who could have been so kind to us?" the fisherman wondered.

"Don't you know?" She looked at him strangely. "Your nephews."

The man spoke low. "But my nephews are with the Otters now."

"They are trying to drown you! Otter People always do! If you hear them whistle outside tonight, you're not to open the door!"

"What sort of man would I be," he said, "to turn away my own little nephews?"

All the same, he was nervous, late that night, when outside the hut they heard a whistle, very low, like an indrawn breath. He jumped to his feet and scowled at his wife and went to unbar the door. Then, squeaking and skittering, in came the boys, and frisking and scuffling, they flitted around the hut. Across the fire they were hard to see, for they were somewhat transparent and faded in and out. The fisherman's wife ran away in horror and hid herself in the corner; but the fisherman, overcome with joy, caught two of them in his arms. But what was this? From the waist up they were the same as always, with laughing little dark

*Canoes (these two painted with Raven and Wolf) were made of single cedar logs and were often large enough for sixty people.*

faces and velvety eyes. But from the waist down they were brown and furry, and their legs were bent like otters'. As they squirmed from his grasp, he saw they had long flat tails growing out behind them. They frolicked around like three little puppies, saying never a word. Then they lay down with their tails near the fire and went to sleep in a pile. The fisherman's wife came out of her corner and touched them with her toe. Soon the fisherman smelled burnt hair, and he leaped up, crying,

> *Get up, get up! You're done to a turn!*
> *Get up! Your tails are starting to burn!*

At this they jumped up, insulted, and ran out of the house.

The fisherman's wife reproached him bitterly. "Now see what you've done! You've frightened our luck away!"

For a time it did seem as if they had seen the last of the boys, and the last of the good luck with them. But the man worked hard to finish his canoe, without telling his wife a word about it.

"Prowling around the woods all day," she scolded. "And me scratching at the beach for what I can find to keep us alive."

Now he had finished hollowing out the canoe. So, filling it with water, he dropped in red-hot rocks. As the wood softened, he could wedge in crosspieces, and he forced in larger and larger wedges until the center was spread. Then he sewed in seats with spruce-root fibers. When he had spent a whole day polishing the sides and rubbing them smooth with sand, he hurried to the beach where his wife was trying to find enough seaweed for supper.

"Never mind supper!" he told the woman, and he pulled her back to the woods, protesting, and showed her the new canoe.

For once the wife had nothing but praise for what he had done. She rapped it with her knuckles, and felt the polished sides, and admired every inch.

"Pick up an end," he said at last. "We'll take it to the beach."

They each took an end and lifted. Nothing happened.

"It's stuck in the dirt," said the man, and he loosened the dirt underneath it. The woman put her arms around one end, and the fisherman locked his fingers under the keel. They strained and heaved, but to no avail. The canoe refused to budge.

That night the fisherman was so discouraged he went to bed without even feeling hungry. But in the night there was a squeaking and a skittering again, and small hands were pulling at his feet. He sat up sharply. Dancing around his bed he saw his three little Otter nephews. They pulled him up and out the door, and running ahead and back like puppies, they led him to the new canoe. He saw that they wanted him to lift his end, and just to show them how heavy it was, he tried. But now the canoe was light as a bird, and the Otter boys slipped their tails underneath it and slid it down to the shore.

"If only we had some bait," thought the fisherman, and right away two stranded devilfish were glimmering in the moonlight. So the three little Otter boys took one paddle, while he sat in the stern with the other. The canoe shot out to the halibut grounds, and the Otter boys helped bait the hooks. Tying all the lines to the seat, they went overboard and slipped underneath the water. They stayed down for a long time, and he knew by the jerking that they were catching fish and attaching them to the hooks. Then they came up and every line was taut. When they pulled them all up they had as much halibut as the new canoe would carry.

The very next night they came again, and soon the storehouse was bursting. The woman cut up fish all day, gloating over their riches. Then she began to want to go home, for what was the good of being rich with no one around to be jealous?

"We'll go," said the man, "but I'm taking along my nephews."

"You can't!" cried the wife. "What would people say if you came home with three little Otters? And they'd die in the daylight."

"Then I'll sleep all day and do my fishing at night."

But he knew he was talking to hear himself talk, and the woman was really right. So he called upon Raven, and Raven came flying and met him at the edge of the woods behind the hut.

"The boys are Otters at night," said Raven, "but all day long they play on an island, with their Otter garments hanging on a bush. Catch them like that, and you'll have your boys again."

And now, every day, every day, every day, the fisherman searched for his nephews. Looking out to sea, he saw hundreds of islands, scattered like a handful of shells. So the unlucky fisherman set out to search them all. It was the last hot spell of the false summer, and his wife kept nagging him to take her home to her friends; but he kept on searching. And at last he saw them.

He had taken the sound of their shouting at first for the shrill little cries of sea birds. But when he rounded the point of the small green island, he could see them playing around a fire, leaping and jumping on little-boy legs, with their Otter skins hung on a bush. So, very softly, he beached his canoe and crept up close to the fire. It was in a sheltered corner out of the wind, and he could smell the salmon his nephews had been cooking. As he watched, they threw the last scraps on the flames and ran to the water to wash the fat from their fingers. Then the fisherman seized the Otter garments and threw them into the fire.

So the man and his wife went home in the new canoe, with the three little nephews perched on a load of fish. The first thing the fisherman did was call on Raven and fill his storehouse. Then he gave a feast for all the people, and they made him one of the head men of the village. His wife was so happy with her new importance that she even forgot to scold. And the three little nephews became the luckiest fishermen ever known at Crooked Beach; but that was because they had played so often on the bottom of the ocean.

*Haida canoe paddle, painted in the typical bold Northwest Coast style.*

# 4 The Nose of the Konakadet

Poor Raven had been hungry since the long-ago day when he had swallowed the shred of bullhead. The people had to keep him supplied with fish, and some of them started to grumble. They forgot he was Raven-Who-Sets-Things-Right, and called him the Greedy-One. As time went on, they brought him less and less, and he lived mostly on scraps he picked up as an ordinary raven, hopping unnoticed under people's feet.

One day Raven was out on the beach in his conjuror's hat, watching the fishermen in the canoes offshore and helping them beach the boats when they were ready. Keeping them company, as he called it; but they knew and he knew he was hoping for bits of fish. He noticed they were using hunks of fat for bait, and, poor thing, his mouth began to water. So he hurried off around the point and changed to his Raven shape. Filling his lungs with a great breath of air, he dived to the bottom and swam underwater to the place where the men were fishing.

The lines wavered down through the dim green water, and at the end of each was a great white lump of fat. Raven unhooked the delicious morsels, and for once he had a satisfying feast.

Up above, the fishermen were distracted. They kept getting bites and catching nothing. But one fisherman, feeling a touch, zipped his line upward as quick as a thought as he felt it give a tug.

Raven was hooked. He was caught by the beak, and though he wriggled and struggled, he was hauled up underneath the man's canoe. Then he gave the bottom a mighty kick, and part of his beak broke off.

The fishermen were deeply puzzled when they brought up the beak.

"It's a shell," said one.

"A piece of slate," said another.

"It's the nose of the Konakadet!"

The Konakadet was the chief of all the fearful monsters who lived on the bottom of the sea. Raven chuckled to hear such talk, but he was anxious just the same. He wanted that beak.

"It's nothing," said a fourth man. "Throw it away! It's only some kind of a mussel."

The shadow of the beak went skimming across the water, and Raven swam out to scoop it up. But just as the beak cut the surface, a Herring darted up to snatch it, and was gone in a train of bubbles. Raven climbed out, bedraggled, on the other side of the point.

He tried to make a new beak out of spruce gum, but it drooped down over his chest. He pushed up his Raven mask and changed to a man; but his hat was split through the center and half of it gone! The hat and the beak were the same thing, so he had broken them both together.

Poor Raven! If he showed himself with half a hat, they would laugh him out of the village. Without it, his shaman's power would be gone. So he changed to a Raven to fly away home, and found that *he could not fly!* By breaking his beak, he had lost his flying power.

The poor old man in half a hat went skulking back to his cottage. All day long he sat in the dark and tried to think what to do. Everything depended on finding his beak, so he would have to go after the Herrings and get it back. The village of the Herring People was far up the coast and there was no way to get there without being able to fly.

He decided to make himself a flying companion, and ride along on its back. But what should it be? An Eagle? A Hawk? He shuddered to think of feeding one of those on his slender rations.

What is it that flies and feeds upon air? He had it! A Butterfly!

So he carved a Butterfly out of yellow cedar, and splashed it with gaudy paint. When he shook his shaman's rattle above it, the Butterfly stirred and trembled on his finger. Slowly it brought its great wings together, and Raven watched it, not daring to breathe, only knowing the creature was alive by the clinging of threadlike legs around his finger. The big damp wings opened wide again, and slowly fanned the air until they dried. Then all at once Butterfly, big as a man, was fluttering in the beam of sunshine under the smoke hole.

"Take on your man shape," said Raven, proud of his creation.

And Butterfly stood there, a handsome young man with cockleshells in his ears. Unhappily, Raven found him slow to learn.

"Listen to me, Butterfly," he told him tartly. "When we find the Herring People, I want you to run ahead of me crying, 'Come out, come out! Here is Raven, the Chief, and he hunts for a sacred object!'"

"Why don't we say we're looking for your beak?" asked Butterfly.

"Never mind!" Raven told him. "Just do as I say, and the Herrings will take me before the Herring Chief."

So Raven mounted Butterfly's back, and they flew up the coast to the town of the Herring People. And when the Herrings saw Raven in half a hat they started to push and giggle. The Chief came out instead of asking him in, and Raven told his errand:

> *We seek a thing long and black and sacred,*
> *Tossed by a fisherman into the ocean,*
> *And carried off by a Herring.*

"Oh, that?" said the Chief. "It was too big for me! I dropped it again, and it was swallowed by a Shark."

On they went to the town of the Shark People, and they smelled on the wind the wonderful smell of a feast.

"The Herrings laughed at the way I look," said Raven in despair. "How can I go to a feast in half a hat? You go, Butterfly, and ask for the beak, but do bring me out some dinner."

So the handsome young man in the shimmering cloak was welcomed by the Sharks and given the seat of honor,

*Tlingit chief's ceremonial headdress representing Shark is made of copper, fur, and sea-lion whiskers.*

while poor old Raven climbed the ladder to the roof and watched the feast through the smoke hole.

"Some tender seal meat?" offered the Chief, and Raven half swooned with pleasure. He knew that Butterfly would bring it all to him, since he never wanted food for himself.

"No, thank you," Butterfly answered. "I never eat seal meat."

"Young fool!" muttered Raven, up on the roof. "He's forgotten me, and I'm empty as a shell!"

"Baked salmon with candlefish sauce?" asked the Shark Chief, and Raven revived at a fine whiff of fish that came curling up through the smoke hole. He thought, "Good! That's better yet!"

41

But, "No, thank you!" Butterfly said serenely. "I never eat it."

Poor Raven almost fell through the smoke hole, watching the dish out of sight. The crooked mouth of the Chief of the Sharks was set in a sour line. But he was determined to please his difficult guest.

"How about cranberries with blueberry cakes?"

"No, thank you. I don't—" But up on the roof came a feeble, "*Ga!*" just loud enough for Butterfly's ear.

"Just a morsel of dried salmon for the journey," Butterfly suggested, and Raven ground his teeth with disappointment. The Shark Chief angrily sent for the salmon and gave Butterfly leave to state his business. And Butterfly said:

*I seek a thing long and black and sacred,*
*Tossed by a fisherman into the ocean,*
*Snatched by a Herring, and swallowed by a Shark.*

"Oh, that?" said the Chief. "It stuck in my teeth. I threw it into the shallow water and saw it seized by a Sea Gull."

Up on the roof, Raven gave a groan and climbed down to join Butterfly, complaining, "As if it wasn't bad enough about my beak, why did you have to ask for this old dried salmon?"

"But you always have it at home!" said Butterfly reproachfully.

So on they went to the town of the Sea Gulls, and Raven sent Butterfly ahead while he rested on the beach. After a bit he came hurrying back, his shadow long on the sand.

"No luck, Raven. They're all in the Chief's house,

dancing and singing. One of them found the Nose of the Konakadet."

"The Nose of the Konakadet! Idiot! That's my beak!"

Raven wrapped up in his dark blanket, and pulled the hat over his eyes. Then, trailed by a line of dogs and children, he went to the house of the Chief and pushed in through the throng. There on the wall was his Raven's beak, hung with sacred eagle feathers!

"Strange!" said the queer old man in the blanket. "May I take it in my hand?" And they let him hold it.

"This house is dark!" the old man complained. "Can't somebody open the smoke hole?" And they pushed aside the boards.

Then, "*Ga, ga, ga!*" Raven clapped on his beak and went whirling up through the hole. And all the Gulls came screaming after, but Raven led them out to sea hunting for a school of fish. At last he spied a wavering patch of darkness under the water. He flew very low, and when he dared to look back, the Gulls were circling over the fish with harsh cries. Then Raven flew home, on his own strong wings, while Butterfly went off to the town of the Insect People. It was getting dark, and the purple sky was streaked with ragged clouds. But Raven followed the foam of the breakers under a misty moon. And when Butterfly told of these adventures, this is the song he sang:

> *We found a thing long and black and sacred,*
> *Tossed by a fisherman into the ocean,*
> *Snatched by a Herring, swallowed by a Shark,*
> *And called by a Sea Gull the Nose of the Konakadet!*

# 5 Cannibal

Raven taught the people of Crooked Beach how to make
bows and arrows. Then they ranged back into the foothills
every fall and learned the taste of venison and bear meat.
But above all they prized the tender meat of the Mountain
Goat, and this was hard to come by. The Mountain Goat
country was high and rugged, and somewhere hidden
among the crags was the house of the Cannibal-of-the-
North-End-of-the-World. Many brave hunters dared enter
that country, but few of them returned, and fewer every
year, until the hunters gave up going there altogether.
Then three young brothers went to Raven.

"Raven," said the eldest, "when I was small, I tasted
the tender meat of the Mountain Goat. My brothers want
to taste it too, so we are off to the Mountain Goat country.
Will you show us the way?"

"The Mountain Goat country is dangerous!" said Raven.
"Haven't you heard of the Cannibal-of-the-North-End-of-
the-World?"

"We know of him," said Eldest Brother. "The Cannibal
ate our father when we were young. We've sworn, if the
Cannibal shows himself, to shoot him through the heart."

"The Cannibal has no heart," said Raven, "and he can't be killed by ordinary methods. He's been drowned in a whirlpool and he's come out alive, and he picks out arrows like burrs."

But the brothers refused to give up their plan, and off they set, the three of them, with their yew-wood bows and arrows. The fourth day they came to rugged country, and toward night they had to admit that they were lost. Seeing a house at the side of the trail, they entered and saw a Woman-Rooted-to-the-Floor. She grew up out of the floor like a tree, and big tears were streaming down her cheeks.

"Alas, my poor children," the woman mourned, "you should never have come to this wild and evil country. Turn back now; don't delay for an hour, or you will be devoured like your father before you."

"How did you know about our father?" asked Eldest Brother, startled; and the woman replied, "Your father stopped here too."

"But we are only hunting Mountain Goats!" protested the youngest.

"The house of the Mountain Goats is beyond the mountain," said the woman. "You will know it by the white smoke billowing out of the smoke hole. But this is a dangerous countryside. Go back!"

And Eldest Brother said, "Perhaps she is right."

"We are strong men," said the youngest. "What should we fear?"

"Go back, go back; I dare not tell you," wept the Woman-Rooted-to-the-Floor, but only the eldest would listen. She kept them with her overnight, and all she would say was,

like an albatross. She served them food, and her fingernails were curved like the claws of a grizzly bear. While the brothers huddled uneasily together, a little boy crept from the corner. Instead of a nose he had a beak like his mother's, and he looked at the brothers and licked his lips like a hungry man looking at his dinner.

Then all of the brothers were seized with terror, and ran pell-mell out of the house. The woman ran after and stood at the door, and called in a terrible voice:

> *Come, Cannibal-of-the-North-End-of-the-World!*
> Hap, hap! *Come, come!*
> *Meat's come to the house,*
> *But now meat's running away!*

And as the brothers ran, they heard, "*Hap, hap, hap!*" and knew it was the Cannibal call. When they could see the giant's topknot bounding along above the screen of trees behind them, the eldest of the brothers threw down the whetstone of Woman-Rooted-to-the-Floor. And at once a high, bare mountain rose behind them. The three brothers dashed on, safe for a moment, while the Cannibal fought his way up the face of the cliff. They heard hoarse breathing as he reached the top, and "*Hap, hap, hap!*" came the Cannibal call, and he was bounding down behind them. Then the second brother dropped the yew-wood comb, and it changed to a forest of yew trees. They heard him sputter as he ripped through the branches, and the brothers ran faster than ever. But, "*Hap, hap, hap!*" he crashed through to the clearing, and the third brother pulled out the stopper of the flask and dribbled the oil behind them. The oil

*Tlingit comb showing
Raven and prey
is carved from cedar,
decorated with shell.*

spread out to make a huge lake, and the Cannibal went floundering around the edges.

The three brothers put a great space between them and the Cannibal, and when they came near home the youngest called upon Raven, saying, "Raven! Save us! The Cannibal-of-the-North-End-of-the-World is treading on our heels!" So Raven dug a pit in his conjuror's hut, and he filled the pit with red-hot rocks and covered it over with a mat.

Then the three brothers were almost home, but the Cannibal leaped the last arm of the lake and came charging down upon them. So the brothers broke up all their arrows, and scattered the pieces behind them as they ran. And the broken arrows became a tangle of tree trunks like a forest ripped by the wind. While the Cannibal struggled to make his way through, the brothers reached the safety of Raven's hut and ran to hide in the dark corners. And Raven went out and greeted the panting Cannibal like a guest.

"Come in!" he said. "I sent the three brothers to invite you!"

The Cannibal entered, blind from the sunlight, and Raven waved him to the seat of honor, beyond the pit full of red-hot rocks. In fell the Cannibal, down on the rocks, and his body was burned to a cinder.

But the ashes sputtered when they carried them out, and cried, "*Hap, hap!* We'll feed on the flesh of all mankind forever!"

And the ashes of the Cannibal whirled away on the wind, to become the gnats, fleas, horseflies, and mosquitoes of future generations.

# 6 The Mountain Goats

When they heard that the Cannibal was gone for good, some tribes moved into the Mountain Goat country and settled there. And the men who lived among those rugged cliffs were as wild and savage as their country. They raided other villages in big war canoes, and burned and looted, and carried home captives as slaves. Once these wild men descended on Crooked Beach, and although the people fought bravely and beat them off, one young son of a chief was carried away and grew up in the mountain country as a slave.

Captured-Man was deeply troubled by the ways of the mountain people. Having learned about what was right from Raven, he knew that animals should only be killed for food or clothing, and the scraps should always be burned. But his masters killed all the mountain goats they could, and left the carcasses lying where they fell. They carried off only the horns for spoons, and a little of the choicest meat. All through the jagged cliffs and canyons, the scattered bones lay bleaching in the sun.

"If we take what we need and burn the scraps, the animal's spirit will recover," Captured-Man told them.

But they refused to listen.

One fall they took a baby goat from its mother, and carried it home as a plaything for the children. And the children, having no more sense than the parents, held it and fondled it and snatched it back and forth, and never let the poor thing rest. The older people heard the children's noise, but they shrugged it off, saying, "It's only that baby goat."

Then Captured-Man shoved the children aside and took the little goat away. "Beware!" he told them. "The Mountain Goat Chief is watching over his people!"

But the children laughed.

Captured-Man kept the little goat overnight, and fed it, and let it rest on his blanket in the corner. In the morning he painted a scratch on its face with his own red face paint, and carried it far away from the village before he turned it loose. The little goat nuzzled his hand for a moment and bounded off.

54

*Captured-Man puppet at right;
behind, a Tlingit staff of a crane
with Captured-Man in its beak.*

The year passed, and the people of the village forgot all
about the children and the baby goat. Then, when the moon
was low and fat, messengers came to invite the hunters to
a feast. The strangers were wrapped in long gray blankets,
and they left when their message was delivered and refused

to have anything to eat. But the mountain people were fond of a feast, and they went into their houses and dressed themselves in their ceremonial garments. They wore headdresses hung with the tails of bears, and one had an earring of abalone and one had a mantle embroidered with puffin beaks.

While the fathers were getting ready for the feast, the children followed the strangers out of town. What was their amazement, then, to see the tall, grim men throw off their blankets and go bounding up the canyon! The children ran home, their eyes popping out with the wonder of what they had seen.

"They've thrown off their blankets and turned into Goats!" they shouted. And the mothers cuffed them and told them to tell the truth.

The men set out, taking Captured-Man with them in case he should be useful. Soon, following the trail that the messengers had pointed out, they came in sight of a great square house with white smoke billowing from the smoke hole. Behind it rose a dark cliff, and it looked as if the house were part of the mountain.

As they drew near, the door opened, and out filed the people wearing long gray blankets and the headdress of the Mountain Goat. Singing and dancing to welcome the strangers to the feast, they made a great circle around the hunters and swept them into the house.

They were seated all together at the front. But one young man wearing red face paint singled out Captured-Man and led him aside. He made him sit in the central space, with his back against a heavy house post. And all through the

56

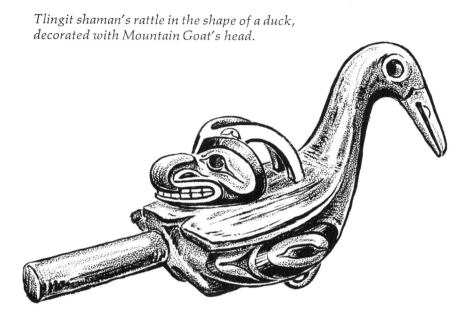

*Tlingit shaman's rattle in the shape of a duck, decorated with Mountain Goat's head.*

serving of the four courses, he watched to see that he had the choicest food. Captured-Man was astonished at this, for he was used to scraps. His masters watched him angrily, but there was nothing they could do.

Then the ceremony started. After singing the songs of the four guardian spirits of the house, they heard the eerie whistling of the winter wind. Then up through the center of the earthen floor came a slender white peak like the icy top of a mountain. It rose until its top went out through the smoke hole, and wide cracks opened in the floor, and the earth shuddered.

While the hunters stared speechless at the mountain in the house, the rattles began to shake. A one-horned Goat appeared upon the mountain, and lightly it leaped from crag to crag down to the level of the people. Then it sailed through the air, just clearing their heads, and struck the front of the house with its cloven hoof.

With a noise like thunder, the house gave way. The whole front wall went sliding down, and the boards were wrenched loose, and the roof pitched downward after the rest, into clouds of smoking rubble.

When silence came at last and the dust had cleared away, Captured-Man found himself outdoors, on the open side of the mountain. The house post behind him had changed to stone, and a dizzy chasm lay at his feet, with the blue sea beating on wicked rocks below. He was pressed against the cliff on a narrow ledge that faded away to nothing on his right. To the left it climbed steeply around the shoulder of the mountain.

But now, as he watched, there came leaping down it a young Goat.

"Have no fear, my friend," said the Mountain Goat. "You rescued me from the children once, so when the Goat Chief killed the wicked hunters, you were saved from the landslide."

Captured-Man shrank from the rocky chasm and covered his eyes.

"How am I ever to get off of this terrible mountain?" he asked.

"I'll lend you my shoes," said the Mountain Goat. "Now watch what I do, and say what you hear me say."

Then, with a "Goat foot leap!" and "Goat foot jump!" and matching the rhythm of the magic words, the Mountain

Goat skipped lightly down the face of the treacherous cliff. He circled back up and let Captured-Man put on his goatskin and his cloven shoes. Trusting in the power of the Mountain Goat's magic, he said, "Goat foot leap!" and his left foot held, and "Goat foot jump!" and his right foot held. Then, "Over the chasm, over the glacier! Leap! Jump! Leap!" And away he went, with the clear sky above him and the wild wind singing in his ears. He leaped down the mountain, free as a goat, free of his masters at last.

Leaving the goatskin and the cloven shoes, Captured-Man returned to the village and called the children together. He led them back to the high places and made them gather up the bleached bones of the goats and burn them.

These boys were better hunters than their fathers, for they followed Raven's advice, never killing without reason, and treating the bones with respect. Captured-Man became Head-Man among them, and the Mountain Goat was the crest of his family for all the generations.

# 7 Strong-Man

Very near Crooked Beach there lived a Chief who had four
sons. The three older boys were strong, and proud of their
strength. Even in the winter, they rose early in the morning
and went for a dip in the ocean, and after they came out
they ran races on the sand, and beat each other with hand-
fuls of twigs until they glowed from head to foot. They
would prove their strength by pulling up small dead cedars
to carry into the house for the breakfast fire. There they
would find their brother asleep, or just sitting up to yawn
and stretch himself on his pile of blankets. "Dirty-Boy,"
they called him, and his father was ashamed because his
youngest son was a weakling. He tried to rout him out of
bed in the morning, but the boy would only grunt and mum-
ble a little and cover his head with the blankets.

"Amala," they called him, meaning "Dirty-Boy," and
the people of the village soon took up the name. The boy
led a miserable life.

But Amala had a reason for sleeping late in the morning.
He was secretly training himself for strength by bathing
in the night. One night in the summer he had gone after
sunset to bathe in a forest pool. With his eyes half shut,

he had floated on his back and watched the first stars come swimming into sight through the dark interlacing branches over his head. He stayed a long time in the cool water, and when he was climbing up the bank he met a short, sturdy man with a bearskin tied around his waist.

"What's this?" growled the man. "A human boy, and you dare to bathe in my magic pool?"

"I didn't know it was yours," said Amala quickly. "I came here to swim and try to make myself strong like my older brothers."

"So you want to be strong?" the man asked him. "Well, I am the Strength-Giver. Step up here and wrestle."

Amala stepped up to the man in fear, for his brothers had told him often enough what a miserable wrestler he was. Just as he had expected, the ground shot up at once and hit him in the back.

"That's not the way," said Strength-Giver crossly. "Here, stand up and I'll show you a few holds."

He gave Amala a lesson in wrestling, and let him bathe himself at the end in the magic pool. After rubbing him all over with a handful of spruce until his skin began to tingle, Strength-Giver told him to come back for more the next night.

So it went on, all through the summer and the fall, and by winter Amala was very strong, but his father and his brothers still thought he was a weakling. One cold night as he ran home wet, feeling the warm strength pounding through his veins, out of sheer high spirits he seized on a little spruce tree and pulled it up by the roots. Then he realized what he had done, and set it back in the ground.

In the morning when his brothers came back from their swimming and were gathering wood for the fire, the eldest brother took hold of the same little spruce tree and lifted it out of the ground. The Head-Man was very proud of his powerful son.

"Wake up, Amala, you weakling!" he said, poking the bundle of blankets with his toe. "Your brother has pulled up a spruce tree, roots and all!"

Next day the people went off in three canoes to hunt sea lions. When Amala asked to go along, his father refused him, but Amala jumped in as his brothers' canoe pulled away. "I am going!" he cried, and the flash of his eye silenced their objections.

They reached the island where the sea lions were basking, spread out on the warm rocks in the winter sun. They were great, meaty creatures, bigger than men, with sparse whiskers sprouting around their mouths. The eldest brother leaped ashore on the rock, and to prove his courage he hurled his harpoon at the largest of the sea lions. Shaking off the spear, the sea lion rushed him and carried him off his feet. He would have been killed if the other brothers had not dragged him, half unconscious, into the boat.

Then Second Brother took up the carved harpoon, and hurled it at the same enormous sea lion. The creature flung itself upon the man, and he wrestled with it, but he would have been crushed against the rock if his younger brothers had not saved him.

The third brother took up the harpoon, trembling, for he knew that his strength was less than that of his brothers. In a moment the sea lion had thrown him, too, and he was

*Haida and Tlingit totem poles.*
*The first and second poles from left*
*show Beaver, traditionally carved with*
*big teeth, stick, and cross-hatched*
*tail. The third pole shows Strong-Man*
*killing a sea lion with his*
*bare hands. On the fourth are*
*(from top) Raven, a man, Shark,*
*Killer Whale. On the sixth,*
*Eagle sits under two small human figures.*

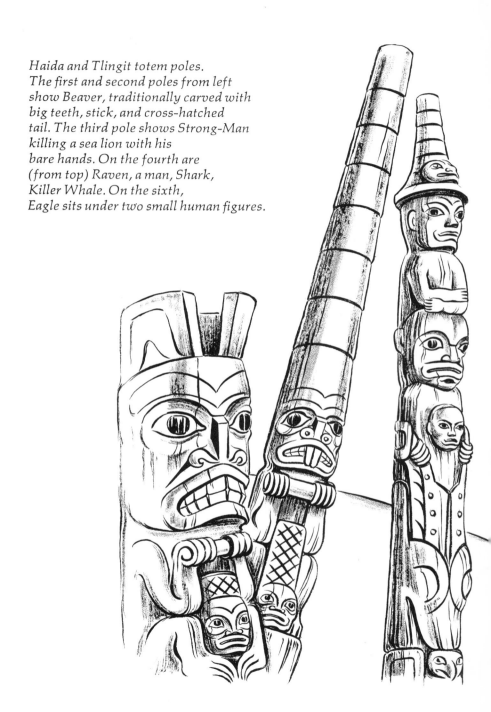

barely able to get back to the safety of the canoe.

But Amala leaped out on the sea lion rock and harpooned the big one, and wrestled with another, and felled a third with his club.

The other hunters were seized with fear when they saw his huge strength and remembered how often they had mocked him in the past.

"Let us leave him," one of them whispered. "Now that he has found his strength, he could kill us all."

They picked up their paddles and went skimming away, leaving Amala on the rock. His brothers were too battered and bruised to realize what they were doing.

But when the tide rose, the rock grew small, and Amala feared that he would drown. So he called upon Raven, and Raven came winging out into the sunset. When he saw the dead sea lions and knew what a mighty fighter Amala had become, he called on the Sun to reward him as a chief. And coasting down the rays of the setting sun came a flashing copper canoe.

Amala paddled home in the copper canoe, and when he laid down his paddles they struck the sides with the sound of a great bell. Then all the people ran down to the beach to marvel at the sight. As Amala stepped ashore, the canoe shot from his grasp and dived beneath the fiery waters, to be seen no more.

Then all the people dropped to their knees to beg his forgiveness. Amala forgave them, and they changed his name to Strong-Man.

From that day on, Strong-Man was the leader of the four

brothers. They swam all together in the glittering ocean, and when the old father died Strong-Man became the Head-Man of the village. And he carved a Sea Lion on his totem pole, and made the Sea Lion the crest of his house for future generations.

*Haida stone carving of Sea Lion floating at its ease.*

# 8 The False Shaman

A young man lived at Crooked Beach who was much too
fond of wasting time with his friends. He liked to play ball
on the beach all day, or throw the gambling sticks, and
he grudged the time it took to catch enough fish to keep
himself alive. But trifling as he was, he was handsome and
kind, and when he fell in love with the Head-Man's
daughter, she fell in love with him, and soon they were
married.

Then the girl's mother was very much put out. She had
wanted a rich young chief for her daughter, and here she
had married the Trifler. The woman fed the young man on
scraps, and when he was late coming home she would say,
"I suppose my son-in-law has been felling me a tree in the
forest!" But she knew he had only been playing ball on
the beach. All this made his poor wife feel very sad.

Then real trouble came. Word ran through the village
like flame through a forest: "The Konakadet is loose!"

The Konakadet was the fearful monster who lived at the
bottom of the sea. Now he was coming ashore in the night
and scooping up people on the beaches. Even in the day-
time he capsized canoes and swallowed the men as they

sank. The people were afraid to go out fishing, and they sat in their houses, hungry. When they went to Raven, he tried all his magic spells; but nothing worked.

At that the ungrateful people turned against him. "Fine shaman you are!" they taunted him. "You'll be the first one to starve!"

But Trifler who had married the Head-Man's daughter never lost faith in Raven. Because of the famine, his mother-in-law was treating him worse than ever. "If you hadn't wasted the summer," she said, "we'd have food in the storehouse now."

At last Trifler went to Raven and told him he was going to attack the Konakadet. And Raven, thin as a wisp, decided to join him.

"But there is danger!" he croaked. "Be ready!"

Trifler tried to quiet his wife's fears, but they left the poor girl weeping. They paddled up the river in Raven's canoe toward a place where the monster had been seen the day before. It was early evening and they both felt glad to get away from the village.

But no sooner had they gone a good long way, when *Glop, glop, glop!* they heard the Konakadet swimming along behind them! They paddled fast, but he gained on them faster, and now, picked out by the setting sun, they could see his copper snout coming around the bend. Then it disappeared, and they knew he was diving to come up underneath and upset the canoe. But just as his head struck the bottom with a thud, they caught hold of a branch that overhung the water, and swung up into a tree.

The canoe capsized with a great splash, and for some

time the monster was busy underwater, looking for Raven and Trifler. But there they sat,
on the branch above the water, hanging on for
dear life. Soon the ripples were broken by a
long lizard head, and the Konakadet waited
until the river lay still and iridescent as a shell.
Then, reflected far beneath the surface, he saw
Raven and Trifler clinging to the tree. With a
snort of rage the monster dived, and spent a
long time underwater. At last his head came
out, and he stared again, and when the surface
cleared he saw Raven and Trifler laughing fit
to kill. So he dived again.

And Raven started to sing the winter song,
to sing the wintertime in. A thin skim of ice
formed over the water, and the pink light
faded, and a wintry moon came up to shine on
the ice. But *crackle, crunch!* the head came
through, and the monster waited in the icy
water until he saw Raven and Trifler, lighted
by the moon, laughing under the water.
A fourth time he dived, and Raven sang so
strongly that it grew colder and colder, and
when the monster's head broke through again,
the ice closed around his neck and held him.
He looked up at Raven and Trifler in the tree,

*Detail from Haida totem pole shows*
*(from top) False Shaman, her son-in-law,*
*and Konakadet.*

and bellowed in his rage.

Raven sang and held him there all night, and when daybreak came he called, *"Ga, ga, ga!"* to drive all the supernatural creatures into their holes. But the monster was caught fast in the ice, and when Raven gave his call, he died. Then Raven flew home to spread the glad news, but no one dared believe that the Konakadet was dead.

Trifler skinned the monster and slipped inside the skin, and it swam with him down to its underwater home. He spent the night admiring his new possessions, abalone and coppers and sea-otter garments. On his way home to bed he caught a salmon and dropped it on the beach. Next morning his mother-in-law went out early and found it.

"Look, husband!" she cried. "What a wife you have! I've found a salmon on the beach!" And she called in her friends to help eat it.

The young man was fast asleep. "That Trifler!" she said.

Next night he left a halibut on the beach. She told people she was seeing spirits, and they believed it, and took her for a shaman.

"What's this?" they asked Raven. "She's a better shaman than you are!" And Raven was sorely puzzled to know how she did it, because Trifler had told him nothing at all, for fear of spoiling the magic.

On the third day the woman found a whale, and she was in a frenzy.

"Carve me a mask!" she commanded. "I am the Food-Giver!"

Finally Trifler tackled two whales at once, and it was a long, hard tussle, even for a monster. Daybreak found him just bringing them ashore. Before he could get out of the skin of the Konakadet, Raven called, and Trifler was caught, and died in the skin of the monster.

Soon after, his mother-in-law came out, and wakened the village with her cries. The people crept out on the rooftops to watch, for they were afraid of the strange monster they saw lying on the sand between the whales. But the woman put on her mask and danced, and she told them the monster was her own Food-Giving-Spirit.

"Then wake up your spirit!" said Raven. "Spirits never die."

She danced and shook her rattle, but the Konakadet lay still.

Then Raven pried open the monster's jaws, and inside was Trifler, dead. So the people turned on the false shaman and took away her mask. And they carved up the two big whales and had a feast.

But the poor young wife went weeping to Raven and told him the whole story. At nightfall she and Raven carried the Konakadet up the river, and Raven said spells and shook his shaman's rattle. And just as the moon came up behind the trees, they heard the monster flopping in the river, and Trifler's voice said, "Come here."

The young wife waded out to him, trembling, and climbed up on the monster's back. And he carried her down to live in splendor in his underwater home. So it was that the Konakadet was transformed into a kindly monster. He brings good luck to all that see him, and now and then he still catches a whale and leaves it on the beach for his friends.

# 9 Eagle Boy

Far down the coast from Crooked Beach there was a village built on a high bluff over the ocean. Flights of Eagles swooped and soared over the beach all day, and now and then, half shutting its wings, a bird would come ripping down through the air and snatch up a fish in its talons. The people of the place detested the Eagles, and tried to drive them away. But one boy, an orphan, never grew tired of seeing them wheel and soar above the ocean. When he and his young brother came in from fishing, they would dump their salmon on the sandbar and let the Eagles have a share. People called the older one Eagle Boy. He played with the Eagles and let them light on his arms, and their wicked talons never tore his skin.

The head men of the village were angry at the boys for sharing their catch with the Eagles. All during the salmon run they scolded them about it, but Eagle Boy said, "The Eagles are my friends." And like most little brothers, the younger one followed along.

But when winter came, the food gave out, and the people were very hungry. Then they turned against the orphan boys and railed at them for having wasted salmon on the

Eagles. The boys had nothing left to eat, and they went to everyone in the village, asking for crusts and crumbs. People shared what they had with the younger brother, but the older boy was often turned away hungry. They refused him, saying, "Let the Eagles you fed last summer feed you now!"

But the young one always tucked away half of what they gave him for his brother—a fin or piece of gristle. The two of them chewed bits of fat all day, and kept themselves alive.

Then Eagle Boy appealed to the Chief, for the Chief always feeds his people when they are hungry. And the Chief said, "Wife, spread a mat by the fire and roast this boy a salmon."

The woman did as she was told, and Eagle Boy sat there, smelling it cook, his first hot food in weeks. She laid it in a dish, all crisp and brown, and the boy stretched out his hands to take it, thinking, "I must remember to save half for my younger brother."

Then the Chief snatched the smoking dish away and said, "Let the Eagles you fed last summer feed you now."

The boy went out, almost faint with hunger, but the Chief's youngest daughter slipped him a bit of meat. She pitied the poor orphan boy, and hated to see him starve. But the whole town was near to starving, and at last the Chief sent out word to the village that they were to move to a distant beach. There he hoped they might live on shellfish and seaweed until spring. So the people gathered up all they had and packed their last bits of meat and fat into their ten canoes.

76

*Haida painted wooden hat representing Eagle, with Killer Whale sticking up at left.*

But Eagle Boy they left behind them, saying, "Let the Eagles you fed last summer feed you now!"

They put out the fires and stamped out the coals and threw water on the ashes. Then the Chief's youngest daughter beckoned Eagle Boy away, around the side of the house. She gave him a dried berry cake, and told him where she had hidden a slow-burning fern root inside a mussel shell, to start his fire.

When all the canoes were packed and ready, Younger Brother was nowhere to be found. They called and peered into all the houses, dark now with a winter chill, with the fires dead and the boards laid over the smoke holes. But the day was passing and the night would come early, and the Chief shouted to his people at last that they would have to set out without him.

Eagle Boy stayed at the edge of the woods until the canoes had faded to specks and disappeared. Then he went back to the deserted village and sat himself down in his empty house, hungry and all alone. The one little berry cake he held in his hand was all he had left to save him from starvation. He raised it to his lips to eat and be done with it, when all of a sudden he felt a fist in his back, and his younger brother was grinning into his face!

"I ran away and hid!" he told Eagle Boy proudly. "I didn't want to go away and leave you."

Now Eagle Boy felt worse than before, because he had never intended that his poor little younger brother should share his fate. He gave him the berry cake to eat for his supper, and ran to dig up the mussel shell with the smoldering coal inside it. When he had his fire going again, he gathered a heap of moss for bed and blanket.

All night long, Eagle Boy had uneasy dreams of the summer, with Eagles wheeling in the glittering sunshine over the piles of fish. Great wings were beating around his head, and talons clutched his arm.

When he woke in the morning he thought he was dreaming still, for he heard the screech of an Eagle down on the beach. Too weary to move, he sent Younger Brother down to see what was going on. The boy came puffing back with a fat little trout that the Eagle had dropped!

Quickly Eagle Boy said to him, "Roast it!" and he gave his brother the whole of it to eat.

Next morning the Eagle screamed again, and the little boy ran to the beach. But he had to shout for Eagle Boy to help him; for this time the Eagles had brought them a halibut as big as Younger Brother. Now Eagle Boy thought they were sure to survive, and he ate all he wanted, and spread out the rest to dry.

Next day they heard two Eagles screaming, and they ran down together, and this time it was a sea lion. They cut up the meat all day on the beach, and packed it away in the storehouse.

On the fourth day the boys woke to the sound of many Eagles screeching. Both of them ran down the path to the beach, and saw Eagles dipping and wheeling over a great bulk close to the shore. They were bringing in a whale! Hurrying to the forest for cedar tips, the boys made a long rope. At high tide they slipped their rope around the whale and tied it firmly to a rock. The next day they started to cut it up, and they filled three houses with blubber.

While they were cutting up the whale, a raven landed on the sand. "Oh, raven!" said Eagle Boy, "I wish you were a man, to carry some meat to the Chief's youngest daughter and tell her that I am alive!"

At that, Raven pushed up his Raven mask and showed his human face.

"Am I not a man?" Raven asked him. "I will deliver your message."

Eagle Boy saw who Raven was, and he gave him a feast of blubber. Then he tied thin strips of meat around his neck and Raven flew away.

The people were starving in the new village; moving had made their condition worse than ever. Raven found the Chief's youngest daughter digging for clams on the beach.

"Oh, raven!" she said, "I wish you were a man, to give me news of Eagle Boy!"

"Am I not a man?" said Raven, pushing up his mask. "Eagle Boy and his brother are rich, and the whole town smells of blubber. They have four storehouses full to bursting; and he sends you this."

The girl ate the bit of whale meat eagerly, and Raven flew away.

When the two eldest daughters of the Chief saw that their sister was chewing a bit of food, they accused her of keeping the clams she found for herself. Then she had to tell them what Raven had said, and they went to their father with the news.

"The boys you deserted are rich, while we are starving!"

The Chief summoned the people together and told them they were going home. He dressed up his two eldest daughters to offer Eagle Boy as wives, only hoping he would let them land after the way he had been treated. So they set out, and from far away they saw a column of green smoke against the sky. The hungry men paddled fast with the smell of whale meat in their nostrils.

Younger Brother saw the flotilla coming, and recognized the canoes.

"Go away!" he shouted, and he said to his brother, "Make them go!"

But Raven, pecking about among the scraps, told him, "The strongest is the most forgiving."

80

*Tlingit magic charm*
*of Eagle,*
*carved from bone.*

Eagle Boy stood at the edge of the beach and shaded his eyes with his hand. He saw the figure of the Chief in the first canoe, and the two eldest daughters dressed in their finest, sitting up high on boxes. But Youngest Daughter was back with the people, and Eagle Boy waved the others aside, saying, "Let Youngest Daughter be the first to land, for she is to be my wife."

Then the people came ashore rejoicing, to enjoy the wedding feast. Soon the tribes came from far and near and traded with Eagle Boy for food. They brought copper shields and sea-otter garments, dancing blankets and canoes. For the bride they brought earrings made of Killer Whales' teeth, spoons and dippers of carved horn, and costly abalone. The Eagles kept bringing whales, seals, sea lions, and halibut, so all his life Eagle Boy was the richest of chiefs. And the Eagle became the crest of his family for future generations.

# 10 The Everlasting House

At Crooked Beach the people were starving again. The wind blew all day every day, and the fish were driven out to sea. Spray beat up over the roofs of the village, and Raven sat hungry inside his house, choking on the smoke that the wind blew back down the smoke hole. Then he put on his wings and flew out to sea, with the strong east wind at his back. When the land was less than a cloud behind him, he saw a house tossing like a box on the ocean, and flew down to circle it, thinking it must have been washed away in the storm.

"This looks likes the finest house in the world," he decided. "There ought to be food inside it for the taking." So he flew down the smoke hole, but he was disappointed to find a man by the fire. The man hid whatever surprise he felt and asked his visitor who he was.

"I am Raven," said the big bird crossly. "Everyone knows me."

"Then I am the only one who does not know you," said the man. When Raven asked who he might be, he answered, "I am a man, and I have been a man since the beginning of time. I have no father, no mother, no sister, and no brother, and I do not know where I come from. But here I am, and here I have been, ever since the world was created."

"Out on the water?" Raven asked him. "What do you find to eat?"

For answer, the man lifted up a floorboard and dropped a fishing line through it. Reflected light poured up through the hole, and a rippling pattern ran across his skin like the scales of a fish. Almost at once the line grew taut, and he pulled up a halibut and clubbed it.

"Do you always have such luck?" Raven asked, and the man nodded in silence. Then he built up the fire to cook the fish, and it sizzled as the golden drops of oil dripped off the crackly skin. Raven devoured his portion quickly, being even more hungry than usual. But when the man threw his scraps down the fishing hole, Raven started back, astonished. It looked to him as if they had changed under water into a school of little fish!

"This house is even better than it looked," he pondered. "Food and shelter all in one. Why should this fellow keep it to himself?"

The Fisherman seemed to read his thoughts. "Raven," he said, "I have no father, no mother, no sister, and no brother, and I have lived alone since the very beginning of time. Would you like to stay here and live with me in my Everlasting House?"

Raven said he would. So he stayed a whole week, and every day he tried to persuade the Fisherman to share his bounty with the people.

"Your Everlasting House is blowing out to sea, and all

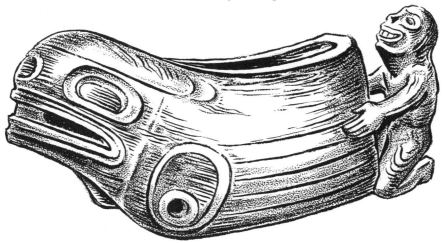

*Kwakiutl wooden feast dish of Whale and harpooner. Such dishes were two to ten feet long.*

the fishes with it," he said. "Bring it closer to the shore and save the people!"

"No!" said the Fisherman. "What do I care for the people?"

At last Raven thought of a desperate scheme. He moped and sighed around the house, until the Fisherman asked what ailed him.

"Alas!" said Raven. "I am lonely for my father, who lives in just such a house as yours, far out on the open ocean."

"I have never had a father," said the Fisherman sadly. "I have no father, no mother, no sister, and no brother, but if I had I should never wish to leave them. So go, Raven! I am used to being alone."

"No," said Raven hastily. "Not unless you will come with me."

The man protested that he could not fly, but Raven took him up and flew slowly around the room until he was reassured. And he told the Fisherman that if he wanted to rest on the way, he would drop a pebble and make him an island to rest on. So they soared through the smoke hole and were caught by the wind and swept out to sea.

"How soon will it be?" the man kept asking fearfully.

Raven said, "Soon!" and then he croaked, "Now!" and dropped the pebble and it changed into a rocky island.

"Swim for it, Fisherman!" Raven cried, and he rolled over and over in the air four times and dropped the man into the ocean. Then he flew back to the Everlasting House and darted in through the smoke hole. He flew once around the shadowy room, gloating over the size of it and the great carved screens at the back. But he was hungry, so he took up the floorboard and dropped his fishing line.

The house was quiet, after the bluster outside, rocking gently with the regular slap of the waves against its bottom. The heavy rafters high above seemed to ripple in the running pattern of light reflected from the water.

Suddenly the fishing line dragged and ran burning through Raven's fingers. The light from below was blotted out as something shot up out of the water and flung itself through the hole. Cold hands fastened around his throat, and Raven looked into the eyes of the Fisherman and knew he was Halibut-Man.

"Stop, stop!" he kept trying to say. "I can explain it all!"

But Halibut clubbed him and threw him into the water.

Raven flew around all night, but in the morning he slipped in quietly again.

"So you're back!" said Halibut, raising his eyes from the fishing and snatching up his club. Just then he had a bite, so he pulled up his line and used the club on the fish. Then Raven was standing there, baiting the hook, as if he had never left.

"I threw you out once," Halibut told him, scowling, but Raven said, "Why talk about me, when we ought to be thinking of the people?"

"What do I care for your people?" said Halibut. "I am a fish!"

"You care for your house, and I found last night that we are close to the whirlpool at the edge of the world. Do you want to go over?"

Halibut was frightened at that, and he summoned the Killer Whales. From every side came the giants of the ocean, spewing water through their blowholes. Wallowing and lolling, they filled the water as far as the eye could see. They laid their big heads against the Everlasting House and carried it along, faster and faster, until they almost ran it ashore at Crooked Beach. Then Halibut opened the carved doors, and water gushed out, leaping with all sorts of fish.

Two little boys were playing on the beach. They saw the Everlasting House offshore, and ran back to the village calling, "Come out! There's a house in the ocean with fish spouting out of the door!"

The people came running, to stare in wonder at the Everlasting House. Raven stood on the totem pole and flapped his mighty wings to bring the house in closer.

"Sing!" called Raven to the Crooked Beach people. "Sing it closer to the shore!" And the people sang, and it rose on a wave and was swept in almost to the breakers.

"Stronger! Stronger!" Raven kept crying. The people sang out loud and strong, sang for the good days of fishing ahead, sang for the end of the famine. And as the people sang, there came a last great gush from the Everlasting House, and out poured salmon, halibut, candlefish, sculpin, and every sort of shellfish, to fill the waters of all the world forever.

*Kwakiutl forehead Raven mask*
*is painted wood*
*with cedar bark fringes.*

# Acknowledgments

For help in locating source material, the author wishes to thank the Huntington Library in New York, the Library of Congress, and the Smithsonian Institution in Washington. Both author and artist are grateful for the advice and guidance of Dr. Frederick J. Dockstader, Director of the Museum of the American Indian/Heye Foundation, New York, and the Curator of the Research Branch, Mr. Vincent Wilcox, as well as the Librarian of the Museum of Modern Art, New York, Miss Pearl Moeller, and Ms. Rosita Worl, herself a Tlingit Indian, who in 1974 helped set up the exhibition of Tlingit culture at Harvard University's Peabody Museum in Cambridge, Massachusetts. The tales used here were collected on the Northwest Coast by John R. Swanton and Franz Boas and published by the Bureau of American Ethnology over half a century ago. Since the incidents of any one story were often met again in a different setting, the author has felt free to make new combinations of her own. All the material may be traced to the following sources:

John R. Swanton, *Tlingit Myths and Texts* (Bulletin #29, 1904–1905, and Bulletin #39, 1909, Bureau of American Ethnology, Smithsonian Institution, Washington, D.C.)

Franz Boas, *Tsimshian Texts and Tsimshian Mythology* (Bulletin #31, 1909–1910, Bureau of American Ethnology, Smithsonian Institution, Washington, D.C.)

Franz Boas, *Bella Bella Tales* (New York: American Folklore Society, 1932)

Philip Drucker, *Cultures of the North Pacific Coast* (San Francisco: Chandler, 1965)

R. F. Spencer, J. Jennings, et al., *Native Americans* (New York: Harper & Row, Publishers, 1965)

Aurel Krause, *The Tlingit Indians*, translated by Erna Gunther (Seattle: University of Washington Press, 1955)

All of the pictures in RAVEN-WHO-SETS-THINGS-RIGHT are the artist's interpretations of existing Northwest Coast Indian objects and designs. Although some of the objects are in private collections and a few of the totem poles are still standing in Canada and the United States, most of the objects, along with others of interest, can be found in the following museums:

Alaska State Museum, Juneau, Alaska
American Museum of Natural History, New York, New York
Brooklyn Museum, Brooklyn, New York
Chicago Natural History Museum, Chicago, Illinois
Museum of the American Indian/Heye Foundation, New York, New York
Museum of Anthropology, University of British Columbia, Vancouver, British Columbia, Canada
Museum of Primitive Art, New York, New York
Portland Art Museum, Portland, Oregon
Royal Art Museum, Toronto, Ontario, Canada
Seattle Museum of Art, Seattle, Washington
Smithsonian Institution, Washington, D.C.
Thomas Burke Memorial–Washington State Museum, Seattle, Washington